CW00644737

The Little Book of

LOVE LYRICS

This publication is not authorised for sale in
the United States of America and/or Canada.

Wise Publications
London/New York/Sydney/Paris/Copenhagen/Madrid

Exclusive distributors:
Music Sales Limited
8/9 Frith Street, London W1V 5TZ, England.
Music Sales Pty Limited
120 Rothschild Avenue
Rosebery, NSW 2018, Australia.

Order No. AM954822
ISBN 0-7119-7823-9
This book © Copyright 1999 by Wise Publications

Book Engraved and designed by Digital Music Art

Cover design by Trickett & Webb

Printed in Great Britain by
Printwise (Haverhill) Limited, Suffolk.

Your Guarantee of Quality
As publishers, we strive to produce every book to the highest commercial
standards. Particular care has been given to specifying acid-free, neutral-sized paper
made from pulps which have not been elemental chlorine bleached. This pulp is from
farmed sustainable forests and was produced with special regard for the environment.
Throughout, the printing and binding have been planned to ensure a sturdy,
attractive publication which should give years of enjoyment.
If your copy fails to meet our high standards, please inform us and we will gladly replace it.

Music Sales' complete catalogue describes thousands of titles and is
available in full colour sections by subject, direct from Music Sales Limited.
Please state your areas of interest and send a cheque/postal order for £1.50 for postage to:
Music Sales Limited, Newmarket Road, Bury St. Edmunds, Suffolk IP33 3YB.

www.internetmusicshop.com

Contents

A Woman In Love

Words and Music by Barry Gibb and Robin Gibb

Life is a moment in space
When the dream is gone
It's a lonelier place.
I kiss the morning goodbye
But deep down inside
You know we never know why.

The road is narrow and long
When eyes meet eyes
And the feeling is strong.
I turn away from the wall
I stumble and fall
But I give you it all.

I am a woman in love
And I'd do anything
To get you into my world
And hold you within
It's a right I defend
Over and over again
What do I do?

With you eternally mine
In love there is
No measure of time
We planned it all at the start
But you and I
Live in each other's heart.

We may be oceans away
You feel my love
I hear what you say.
The truth is ever a lie
I stumble and fall
But I give you it all.

I am a woman in love
And I'd do anything
To get you into my world
And hold you within
It's a right I defend
Over and over again
What do I do?

I am a woman in love
and I'm talkin' to you
I know how you feel
What a woman can do
It's a right I defend
Over and over again.

I am a woman in love
And I'd do anything
To get you into my world
And hold you within
It's a right I defend
Over and over again.

Could It Be Magic

Words and Music by Barry Manilow and Adrienne Anderson

Spirit moves me
Ev'ry time I'm near you
Whirling like a cyclone in my mind.

Sweet Melissa
Angel of my lifetime
Answer to all answers I can find.

Baby I love you.

Come, come, come into my arms
let me know the wonder of all of you

Baby I want you.

Now, now, now and hold on fast
Could this be the magic at last?

Lady, take me
High up on a hillside
High up where the stallion meets the sun.

I could love you
Building my world around you
Never leave you 'till my life is done.

Could it be magic?

Come, come, come into my arms
let me know the wonder of all of you

Baby I want you.

Now, now, now and hold on fast
Could this be the magic at last?

Dedicated To The One I Love

Words and Music by Lowman Pauling and Ralph Bass

While I'm far away from you my baby
I know it's hard for you my baby
Because it's hard for me my baby
And the darkest hour is just before dawn.

Each night before you go to bed my baby
Whisper a little prayer for me my baby
And tell all the stars above
'This is dedicated to the one I love'.

Life can never be exactly like we want it to be.
I could be satisfied knowing you love me.
If there's one thing I want you to do
especially for me
And it's something that ev'rybody needs.

While I'm far away from you my baby
Whisper a little prayer for me my baby
Because it's hard for me my baby
And the darkest hour is just before dawn.

If there's one thing I want you to do
especially for me
And it's something that ev'rybody needs.

Each night before you go to bed my baby
Whisper a little prayer for my baby
And tell all the stars above
'This is dedicated to the one I love'.

This is dedicated
This is dedicated to the one I love
This is dedicated
This is dedicated.

Have I Told You Lately

Words and Music by Van Morrison

Have I told you lately that I love you
Have I told you there's no-one above you
Fill my heart with gladness
Take away my sadness
Ease my troubles that's what you do.

Oh the morning sun in all its glory
Greets the day with hope and comfort too
And you fill my life with laughter
You can make it better
Ease my troubles that's what you do.

There's a love that's divine
And it's yours and it's mine
Like the sun at the end of the day
We should give thanks and pray to the one.

Have I told you lately that I love you
Have I told you there's no-one above you
Fill my heart with gladness
Take away my sadness
Ease my troubles that's what you do.

There's a love that's divine
And it's yours and it's mine
Like the sun at the end of the day
We will give thanks and pray to the one.

Have I told you lately that I love you
Have I told you there's no-one above you
Fill my heart with gladness
Take away my sadness
Ease my troubles that's what you do.

Fill my heart with gladness
Take away my sadness
Ease my troubles that's what you do.

Fill my heart with gladness
Take away my sadness
Ease my troubles that's what you do.

How Deep Is Your Love

Words and Music by Barry Gibb, Robin Gibb and Maurice Gibb.

I know your eyes in the morning sun
I feel you touch me in the pouring rain
And the moment that you wander far from me
I wanna feel you in my arms again

And you come to me on a summer breeze
Keep me warm in your love
Then you softly leave
And it's me you need to show

How deep is your love?
I really mean to learn
'Cause we're living in a world of fools
Breaking us down
When they all should let us be
We belong to you and me.

I believe in you
you know the door to my very soul
You're the light in my deepest darkest hour
You're my saviour when I fall

And you may not think I care for you
When you know down inside that I really do
And it's me you need to show

How deep is your love?

I Will Always Love You

Words and Music by Dolly Parton

If I should stay
I would only be in your way
So I'll go, but I know
I'll think of you each step of the way

And I will always love you
I will always love you.

Bitter sweet memories
That's all I am taking with me
Goodbye, please don't cry
We both know that I'm not what you need.

But I will always love you
I will always love you.

I hope that life treats you kind
And I hope that you have
All that you ever dreamed of
And I wish you joy and happiness
but above all this
I wish you love.

And I will always love you
I will always love you
I will always love you.

If I Fell

Words and Music by John Lennon and Paul McCartney

If I fell in love with you
Would you promise to be true
And help me understand
'Cause I've been in love before
And I found that love was more
Than just holding hands.

If I give my heart to you
I must be sure
From the very start
That you would love me more than her.

If I trust in you
Oh please don't run and hide
If I love you too
Oh please don't hurt my pride like her.

'Cause I couldn't stand the pain
And I would be sad
If our new love was in vain.

So I hope you see that I
Would love to love you
And that she will cry
When she learns we are two.

'Cause I couldn't stand the pain
And I would be sad
If our new love was in vain.

So I hope you see that I
Would love to love you
And that she will cry
When she learns we are two.

If I fell in love with you.

Just The Two Of Us

Words and Music by Ralph MacDonald, William Salter and Bill Withers

I can see the crystal raindrops fall
And the beauty of it all
Is when the sunshine comes shining through
To make those rainbows in my mind
When I think of you sometime
And I want to spend some time with you.

Just the two of us
We can make it if we try
Just the two of us
(Just the two of us)

Just the two of us
Building castles in the sky
Just the two of us
You and I.

We look for love, no time for tears
Wasted water all that is
And it don't make flowers grow
Good things might come to those who wait
Not for those who wait too late
We gotta go for all we know.

Just the two of us
We can make it if we try
Just the two of us
(Just the two of us)

Just the two of us
Building castles in the sky
Just the two of us
You and I.

I hear the crystal raindrops fall
On the window down the hall
And it becomes the morning dew
And darlin' when the morning comes
And I see the morning sun
I want to be the one with you.

Just the two of us
We can make it if we try
Just the two of us
(Just the two of us)

Just the two of us
Building castles in the sky
Just the two of us
You and I.

Killing Me Softly With His Song

Words by Norman Gimbel   Music by Charles Fox

Strumming my pain with his fingers
Singing my life with his words
Killing me softly with his song
Killing me softly with his song
Telling my whole life with his words
Killing me softly with his song.

I heard he sang a good song
I heard he had a smile
And so I came to see him and listen for a while
And there he was this young boy
A stranger to my eyes.

Strumming my pain with his fingers
Singing my life with his words
Killing me softly with his song
Killing me softly with his song
Telling my whole life with his words
Killing me softly with his song.

I felt all flushed with fever
Embarrassed by the crowd
I felt he found my letters
And read each one out loud
I prayed that he would finish
But he just kept right on.

Strumming my pain with his fingers
Singing my life with his words
Killing me softly with his song
Killing me softly with his song
Telling my whole life with his words
Killing me softly with his song.

Lay, Lady, Lay

Words and Music by Bob Dylan

Lay, lady, lay
Lay across my big brass bed
Lay, lady, lay
Lay across my big brass bed.

Whatever colours you have
In your mind
I'll show them to you
And you'll see them shine.

Lay, lady, lay
Lay across my big brass bed
Stay, lady, stay
Stay with your man a while.

Until the break of day
Let me see you make him smile
His clothes are dirty but his hands are clean
And you're the best thing that he's ever seen.

Stay, lady, stay
Stay with your man a while.

Why wait any longer for the world to begin
You can have your cake and eat it too
Why wait any longer for the one you love
When he's standing in front of you.

Lay, lady, lay
Lay across my big brass bed
Stay, lady, stay
Stay while the night is still ahead.

I long to see you in the morning light
I long to reach for you in the night
Stay, lady, stay
Stay while the night is still ahead.

Love Is All Around

Words and Music by Reg Presley

I feel it in my fingers
I feel it in my toes
The love that's all around me
And so the feeling grows.

It's written on the wind
It's everywhere I go
So if you really love me
Come on and let it show.

You know I love you, I always will
My mind's made up by the way that I feel
There's no beginning, there'll be no end
'cause on my love, you can depend.

I see your face before me
As I lay on my bed
I cannot get to thinking
Of all the things you said.

You gave your promise to me
And I give mine to you
I need someone beside me
In everything I do.

You know I love you, I always will
My mind's made up by the way that I feel
There's no beginning, there'll be no end
'cause on my love, you can depend.

Got to keep it moving.

It's written in the wind
Oh everywhere I go
So if you really love me
come on and let it show.

Love Letters

Words by Edward Heyman   Music by Victor Young

The sky may be starless
The night may be moonless
but deep in my heart there's a glow
For deep in my heart I know that you love me
You love me because you told me so!

Love letters straight from your heart
Keep us so near while apart
I'm not alone in the night
When I can have all the love you write
I memorise ev'ry line
I kiss the name that you sign
And, darling, then I read again right from the
start
Love letters straight from your heart.

Love letters straight from your heart
Keep us so near while apart
I'm not alone in the night
When I can have all the love you write
I memorise ev'ry line
I kiss the name that you sign
And, darling, then I read again right from the
start
Love letters straight from your heart.

Mona Lisa

Words and Music by Jay Livingston and Ray Evans

In a villa in a little old Italian town
Lives a girl whose beauty shames the rose
Many yearn to love her but their hopes all tumble
down
What does she want?
No one knows!

Mona Lisa, Mona Lisa, men have named you
You're so like the lady with the mystic smile
Is it only 'cause you're lonely they have blamed
you
For that Mona Lisa strangeness in your smile?

Do you smile to tempt a lover, Mona Lisa
Or is this your way to hide a broken heart?
Many dreams have been brought to your doorstep
They just lie there, and they die there

Are you warm, are you real, Mona Lisa
Or just a cold and lonely, lovely work of art?

Michelle

Words and Music by John Lennon and Paul McCartney

Michelle
Ma belle
These are words that go together well
My Michelle.

Michelle
Ma belle
Sont les mots qui vont trés bien ensemble
trés bien ensemble.

I love you, I love you, I love you
That's all I want to say
Until I find a way
I will say the only words I know
That you'll understand.

Michelle
Ma belle
Sont les mots qui vont trés bien ensemble
trés bien ensemble.

I need to, I need to, I need to
I need to make you see
Oh, what you mean to me
Until I do, I'm hoping you will know what I
mean.

I love you.

I want you, I want you, I want you
I think you know by now
I'll get to you somehow
Until I do, I'm telling you so you'll understand.

Michelle
Ma belle
Sont les mots qui vont trés bien ensemble
trés bien ensemble.

And I will say the only words I know that you'll
understand
My Michelle.

One Moment In Time

Words and Music by Albert Hammond and John Bettis

Each day I live I want to be
A day to give the best of me
I'm only one but not alone
My finest day is yet unknown.

I broke my heart for ev'ry gain
To taste the sweet I faced the pain
I rise and fall yet through it all
This much remains.

I want one moment in time
When I'm more than I thought I could be
When all of my dreams are a heartbeat away
And the answers are all up to me.

Give me one moment in time
When I'm racing with destiny
Then in that one moment in time
I will feel
I will feel eternity.

I've lived to be the very best
I want it all no time for less
I've laid the plans now lay the chance
Here in my hands.

Give me one moment in time
When I'm more than I thought I could be
When all of my dreams are a heartbeat away
And the answers are all up to me.

Give me one moment in time
When I'm racing with destiny
Then in that moment in time
I will feel
I will feel eternity.

You're a winner
For a lifetime
If you seize that one moment in time
Make it shine.

Give me one moment in time
When I'm more than I thought I could be
When all of my dreams are a heartbeat away
And the answers are all up to me.

Give me one moment in time
When I'm racing with destiny
Then in that one moment in time
I will be, I will be
I will be free.

I will be
I will be free.

Softly Whispering I Love you

Words and Music by Roger Cook and Roger Greenaway

Softly whispering I love you
Echoes of your voice still from my dreams
Softening the chill of the breeze
Through my window I can see the moon glow
Painting silver shadows on a rose coloured land
A world that we walk hand in hand
In a day of gold coloured by the glow of new love.

I can feel your warm face ever close to my lips
And the scent of you invades the cool evening air
I can close my eyes and you're there in my arms still
Oh I know your soft kiss
Turning into music every beat of my heart
When I hold you close to my heart
And I hear your voice
Whispering I love you.

I can feel your warm face ever close to my lips
And the scent of you invades the cool evening air
I feel you there in my arms still
I know your soft kiss
It's turning into music every beat of my heart
And I hear your voice
Whispering I love you.

I feel you there in my arms still
I can't forget I love you.

Speak Softly Love

Music by Nino Rota   Words by Larry Kusik

Speak softly, love
And hold me warm against your heart.
I feel your words
The tender trembling moments start.

We're in a world
Our very own
Sharing a love that only
Few have ever known.

Wine coloured days
Warmed by the sun
Deep velvet nights
When we are one.

Speak softly love
So no one hears us but the sky
The vows of love we make
Will live until we die.

My life is yours
And all because
You came into my world
With love so softly, love.

Take My Breath Away

Words by Tom Whitlock   Music by Giorgio Moroder

Watching ev'ry motion
In my foolish lover's game
On this endless ocean
Fin'lly lovers know no shame.

Turning and returning
To some secret place inside
Watching in slow motion
As you turn around and say.

"Take my breath away."
"Take my breath away."

Watching, I keep waiting
Still anticipating love
Never hesitating
To become the fated ones.

Turning and returning
To some secret place to hide
Watching in slow motion
As you turn my way and say.

"Take my breath away."

Through the hourglass I saw you
In time, you slipped away
When the mirror crashed I called you
And turned to hear you say.

"If only for today
I am unafraid
Take my breath away
Take my breath away."

Watching ev'ry motion
In my foolish lover's game
Haunted by this notion
Somewhere there's a love in flames.

Turning and returning
To some secret place inside
Watching in slow motion
As you turn to me and say.

"Take my breath away
My love, take my breath away
My love, take my breath away."

The Power Of Love

Words and Music by C Deruge, G Mende, J Rush and S Applegate

The whispers in the morning
Of lovers sleeping tight
Are rolling by like thunder now
As I look in your eyes.
I hold on to your body
And feel each move you make
Your voice is warm and tender
A love that I could not forsake.

'Cause I'm your lady
And you are my man
Whenever you reach for me
I'll do all that I can.

Lost is how I'm feeling
Lying in your arms
When the world outside's too much to take
That all ends when I'm with you.
Even though there may be times
It seems I'm far away
Never wonder where I am
'Cause I am always by your side.

'Cause I'm your lady
And you are my man
Whenever you reach for me
I'll do all that I can.

We're heading for something
Somewhere I've never been
Sometimes I'm frightened but I'm ready to learn
Of the power of love.

The sound of your heart beating
Made it clear suddenly
The feeling that I can't go on
Is light years away.

'Cause I'm your lady
And you are my man
Whenever you reach for me
I'll do all that I can.

We're heading for something
Somewhere I've never been
Sometimes I'm frightened but I'm ready to learn
Of the power of love.

The power of love
The power of love
Sometimes I'm frightened but I'm ready to learn
The power of love.

The Very Thought Of You

Words and Music by Ray Noble

I don't need your photograph
To keep by my bed
Your picture is always in my head.

I don't need your portrait dear
To call you to mind
For sleeping or waking, dear, I find;

The very thought of you
And I forget to do
The little ordinary things
That everyone ought to do.

I'm living in a kind of daydream
I'm happy as a king
And foolish tho' it may seem
To me that's everything.

The mere idea of you
The longing here for you
You'll never know how slow
The moments go 'til I'm near to you.

I see your face in ev'ry flower
Your eyes in stars above
It's just the thought of you
The very thought of you, my love.

I hold you responsible
I'll take it to the law
I never have felt like this before.

I'm sueing for damages
Excuses won't do
I'll only be satisfied with you;

The very thought of you
And I forget to do
The little ordinary things
That everyone ought to do.

I'm living in a kind of daydream
I'm happy as a king
And foolish tho' it may seem
To me that's everything.

The mere idea of you
The longing here for you
You'll never know how slow
The moments go 'til I'm near to you.

I see your face in ev'ry flower
Your eyes in stars above
It's just the thought of you
The very thought of you, my love.

There I've Said It Again

Words and Music by Redd Evans and Dave Mann

I think I've talked too much already
Yet the words continue to flow
And when I place them all together
They still seem to say "I love you so".

I've said it
What more can I say?
Believe me
There's no other way.
I love you
No use to pretend
There! I've said it again.

I've said it
There's nothing to hide
It's better
Than burning inside
I love you
I will to the end
There! I've said it again.

I've tried to drum up a phrase
That would sum up all I feel for you
But what good are phrases?
The thought that amazes is you love me
And it's heavenly.

Forgive me
For wanting you so
But one thing
I want you to know
I've loved you
Since heaven knows when
There! I've said it again.

I've said it
What more can I say?
Believe me
There's no other way.
I love you
No use to pretend
There! I've said it again.

I've said it
There's nothing to hide
It's better
Than burning inside
I love you
I will to the end
There! I've said it again.

This Guy's In Love With You

Words by Hal David   Music by Burt Bacharach

You see this guy
This guy's in love with you
Yes I'm in love
Who looks at you the way I do?

When you smile I can tell
We know each other very well
How can I show you
I'm glad I got to know you

'Cause I've heard some talk
They say you think I'm fine.
This guy's in love
And what I'd do to make you mine

Tell me now, is it so?
Don't let me be the last to know
My hands are shaking
Don't let my heart keep breaking

'Cause I need your love
I want your love
Say you're in love
In love with this guy
If not I'll just die.

'Cause I've heard some talk
They say you think I'm fine
This guy's in love
And what I'd do to make you mine

Tell me now, is it so?
Don't let me be the last to know
My hands are shaking
Don't let my heart keep breaking

'Cause I need your love
I want your love
Say you're in love
In love with this guy
If not I'll just die.

Tonight I Celebrate My Love

Words and Music by Michael Masser and Gerry Goffin

Tonight I celebrate my love for you
It seems the natural thing to do
Tonight no one's gonna find us
We'll leave the world behind us
When I make love to you.

Tonight I celebrate my love for you
And hope that deep inside you feel it too
Tonight our spirits will be climbing
To a sky lit up with diamonds
When I make love to you tonight.

Tonight I celebrate my love for you
And the midnight sun
Is gonna come shining through.

Tonight there'll be no distance between us
What I want most to do
Is to get close to you.

Tonight I celebrate my love for you
And soon this old world will seem brand new
Tonight we will both discover
How friends turn into lovers
When I make love to you.

Tonight I celebrate my love for you
And the midnight sun
Is gonna come shining through.

Tonight there'll be no distance between us
What I want most to do
Is to get close to you.

Tonight I celebrate my love for you
Tonight.

Try A Little Tenderness

Words and Music by Harry Woods, Jimmy Campbell and Reg Connelly

In the bustle of today
We're all inclined to miss
Little things that mean so much
A word, a smile, a kiss.

When a woman loves a man
He's a hero in her eyes
And a hero he can always be
If he'll just realise.

She may be weary
Women do get weary
Wearing the same shabby dress
And when she's weary
Try a little tenderness.

You know she's waiting
Just anticipating
Things she may never possess.
While she's without them
Try a little tenderness.

It's not just sentimental
She has her grief and care
And a word that's soft and gentle
Makes it easier to bear.

You won't regret it
Women don't forget it
Love is their whole happiness.
It's all so easy
Try a little tenderness.

With a tender word of love
You can make the wrong things right
Charm away the clouds of grey
And make this drab world bright.

When your worries drag you down
It's so easy to forget
But make the effort just the same
And see the thrill you'll get.

Unchained Melody

Words by Hy Zaret   Music by Alex North

Oh, my love
My darling
I've hungered for your touch
A long, lonely time.

Time goes by
So slowly
And time can do so much
Are you still mine?

I need your love
I need your love
God speed your love to me!

Lonely rivers flow
To the sea
To the sea
To the open arms of the sea.

Lonely rivers sigh
"Wait for me"
"Wait for me"
I'll be coming home, wait for me!

Oh, my love
My darling
I've hungered for your touch
A long, lonely time.

Time goes by
So slowly
And time can do so much
Are you still mine?

I need your love
I need your love
God speed your love to me!

Lonely mountains gaze
At the stars
At the stars
Waiting for the dawn of the day.

All alone I gaze
At the stars
At the stars
Dreaming of my love far away.

Oh, my love
My darling
I've hungered for your touch
A long, lonely time.

Time goes by
So slowly
And time can do so much
Are you still mine?

I need your love
I need your love
God speed your love to me!

Up Where We Belong

Words and Music by Jack Nitzsche, Will jennings and Buffy Sainte Marie

Who knows what tomorrow brings
In a world
Few hearts survive.

All I know is the way I feel
When it's real
I keep it alive.

The road is long
There are mountains in our way
But we climb a step ev'ry day.

Love lift us up where we belong
Where the eagles cry
On a mountain high
Love lift us up where we belong
Far from the world we know
Up where the clear winds blow.

Some hang on to "Used to be"
Live their lives
Looking behind.

All we have is here and now
All our life
Out there to find.

The road is long
There are mountains in our way
But we climb them a step ev'ry day.

Love lift us up where we belong
Where the eagles cry
On a mountain high
Love lift us up where we belong
Far from the world we know
Up where the clear winds blow.

Time goes by
No time to cry
Life's you and I
Alive
Today.

Love lift us up where we belong
Where the eagles cry
On a mountain high
Love lift us up where we belong
Far from the world we know
Up where the clear winds blow.

When I Need You

Words and Music by Albert Hammond and Carole Bayer Sager

When I need you
I just close my eyes and I'm with you
And all that I so want to give you
It's only a heart beat away.

When I need love
I hold out my hands and I touch love
I never knew there was so much love
Keeping me warm night and day.

Miles and miles of empty space in between us
A telephone can't take the place of your smile
Oh but you know I won't be travelling for ever
it's cold out, but hold out, and do what I do.

When I need you
I just close my eyes and I'm with you
And all that I so want to give you baby
It's only a heartbeat away.

It's not easy when the road is your driver
honey that's a heavy load that we bear
Oh but you know I won't be travelling a lifetime
it's cold out, but hold out, and do like I do.

When I need love
I hold out my hands and I touch love
I never knew, oh never knew there was so much love
Keeping me warm night and day.

When I need you
I just close my eyes and I'm with you
And all that I so want to give you
It's only a heart beat away.

When You're Young And In Love

Words and Music by Van McCoy

Spring's in the air
(Filled with love)
there's magic everywhere
When you're young and in love.

Life seems to be
(Just a dream)
A world of fantasy
When you're young and in love.

Each night seems just like
The Fourth of July
With stars that spangle the sky.

The moon at night
(Shines so bright)
Seems to shine twice as bright
When you're young and in love.

Dreams can come true
(Try a dream)
If you believe they do
When you're young and in love.

So many teardrops
Are bound to fall
true love can conquer all.

When you're
When you're young and in love
trust and you'll find
Oh there's no mountain you can't climb
When you're young and in love.

Tho' many teardrops
Are bound to fall
True love can conquer all
Springs in the air
There's magic everywhere
When you're young and in love.

Dreams can come true
(Try a dream)
If you believe they do
When you're young and in love.

So many teardrops
Are bound to fall
true love can conquer all.

When you're
When you're young and in love
Young and in love
Young and in love
Young and in love.

Without You

Words and Music by Peter Ham and Tom Evans

No, I can't forget this evening
Or your face as you were leaving
But I guess that's just the way the story goes
You always smile but in your eyes the sorrow
shows
yes it shows.

No I can't forget tomorrow
When I think of all my sorrow
And I had you there but then I let you go
And now it's only fair that I should let you know
What you should know.

I can't live
If living is without you
I can't live
I can't give anymore.

I can't live
If living is without you
I can't give
I can't give anymore.

No, I can't forget this evening
Or your face as you were leaving
But I guess that's just the way the story goes
You always smile but in your eyes your sorrow
shows

yes it shows.

I can't live
If living is without you
I can't live
I can't give anymore.

I can't live
If living is without you
I can't give
I can't give anymore.

Woman

Words and Music by John Lennon

Woman, I can hardly express
My mixed emotions at my thoughtlessness
After all, I'm forever in your debt.

And woman, I will try to express
My inner feelings and thankfulness
For showing me the meaning of success.

Woman, I know you understand
The little child inside the man
Please remember, my life is in your hands.

And woman, hold me close to your heart
However distant, don't keep us apart
After all, it is written in the stars.

Woman please let me explain
I never meant to cause you sorrow or pain
So let me tell you again and again and again.

I love you
Yeah, yeah
Now and forever.

I love you
Yeah, yeah
Now and forever.

Words

Words and Music by Barry Gibb, Robin Gibb and Maurice Gibb

Smile an everlasting smile
A smile could bring you near to me
Don't ever let me find you gone
'cause that would bring a tear to me.

This world has lost its glory
Let's start a brand new story now, my love
Right now, there'll be no other time
And I can show you how, my love.

Talk in everlasting words
And dedicate them all to me
And I will give you all my life
I'm here if you should call to me.

You think that I don't even
Mean a single word I say
It's only words, and words are all I have
To take your heart away.

It's only words, and words are all I have
To take your heart away.

It's only words, and words are all I have
To take your heart away.

Wonderful Tonight

Words and Music by Eric Clapton

It's late in the evening
She's wond'ring what clothes to wear
She puts on her make-up
And brushes her long blonde hair
And then she asks me
"Do I look all right?"
And I say
"Yes, you look wonderful tonight."

We go to a party
And everyone turns to see
This beautiful lady
Is walking around with me
And then she asks me
"Do you feel all right?"
And I say
"Yes, I feel wonderful tonight."

I feel wonderful
Because I see
The love light in your eyes
Then the wonder of it all
Is that you just don't realise
How much I love you.

It's time to go home now
And I've got an aching head
So I give her the car keys
And she helps me to bed
And then I tell her
As I turn out the light
I say
"My darling, you are wonderful tonight."

"Oh my darling, you are wonderful tonight."

You Are The Sunshine Of My Life

Words and Music by Stevie Wonder

You are the sunshine of my life
That's why I'll always be around
You are the apple of my eye
Forever you'll stay in my heart.

I feel like this is the beginning
'Though I've loved you for a million years
And if I thought our love was ending
I'd find myself drowning in my own tears.

You are the sunshine of my life
That's why I'll always be around
You are the apple of my eye
Forever you'll stay in my heart.

You must have known that I was lonely
Because you came to my rescue
And I know that this must be heaven
How could so much love be inside of you?

You are the sunshine of my life
That's why I'll always be around
You are the apple of my eye
Forever you'll stay in my heart.

You're Still The One

Words and Music by Shania Twain and Robert John "Mutt" Lange

Looks like we made it
Look how far we've come my baby
We might have took the long way
We knew we'd get there some day.

They said "I bet they'll never make it"
But just look at us holding on
We're still together
Still going strong.

You're still the one I run to
The one that I belong to
You're still the one I want for life
You're still the one I love
The only one I dream of
You're still the one I kiss goodnight

Ain't nothing better
We beat the odds together
I'm glad we didn't listen
Look at what we would be missing.

They said "I bet they'll never make it"
But just look at us holding on
We're still together
Still going strong.

Your Song

Words and Music by Elton John and Bernie Taupin

It's a little bit funny
This feeling inside
I'm not one of those
Who can easily hide
I don't have much money
But boy, if I did
I'd buy a big house where
We both could live.

If I was a sculptor
But then again no
Or a man who makes potions
In a travellin' show
I know it's not much
But it's the best I can do
My gift is this song
And this one's for you.

And you can tell everybody
This is your song
It may be quite simple
But now that it's done
I hope you don't mind
I hope you don't mind
That I put down in words
How wonderful life is
While you're in the world.

I sat on the roof
And kicked off the moss
Well a few of the verses
Well they've got me quite cross
But the sun's been quite kind
While I wrote this song
It's for people like you
That keep it turned on.

So excuse me forgetting
But these things I do
You see I've forgotten
If they're green or they're blue
Anyway the thing is
What I really mean
Yours are the sweetest eyes
I've ever seen.

And you can tell everybody
This is your song
It may be quite simple
But now that it's done
I hope you don't mind
I hope you don't mind
That I put down in words
How wonderful life is
While you're in the world.

For full piano-vocal-guitar arrangements for many more great love songs, try the selection below or see the full Music Sales catalogue (details on P2).

Love Songs: The Number One Hits

A dozen chart-topping love songs as performed by top artists including Bryan Adams, Chris De Burgh and Whitney Houston.
Order No. AM91112

Love Songs: The Number One Hits Volume 2

Order No. AM92061

100 Love Songs

Romantic songs made famous by the greatest singers and artists. Includes Elton John, Nat King Cole and Stevie Wonder.
Order No. AM33853

100 Ballads

A sentimental journey through the world's greatest ballads. Piano/vocal, lyrics and chord symbols.
Order No. AM68123

New Love Songs

15 modern love songs, including Paul Weller "You Do Something To Me', E-17 'Each Time', Steps 'Heartbeat', and The Corrs 'What Can I Do'.
Order No. AM959299